THE ART OF MINDFULNESS

REFRESHED AND INSPIRED COLOURING

Michael O'Mara Books Limited

First published in Great Britain in 2016 by
Michael O'Mara Books Limited
9 Lion Yard
Tremadoc Road
London SW4 7NQ

A CIP catalogue record for this book is available from the British Library.

Papers used by Michael O'Mara Books Limited are natural, recyclable products
made from wood grown in sustainable forests. The manufacturing processes
conform to the environmental regulations of the country of origin.

ISBN: 978-1-78243-631-7

1 2 3 4 5 6 7 8 9 10

www.mombooks.com

Designed by Ana Bjezancevic and Claire Cater

Illustrations by Andy Naidu, Angelika Scudamore, Ela Jarzabek,
Gavin Rutherford, Giovana Medeiros, Hannah Davies, Lizzie Preston,
Lizzy Doyle, Pimlada Phuapradit, Victoria Nelson and Zoe Connery

Cover illustration by Gavin Rutherford

Printed and bound in China

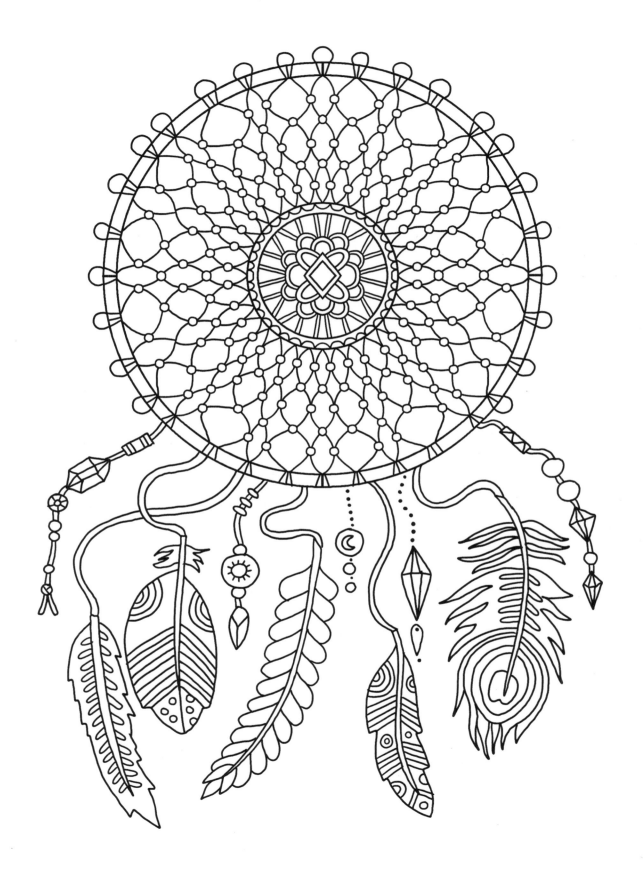

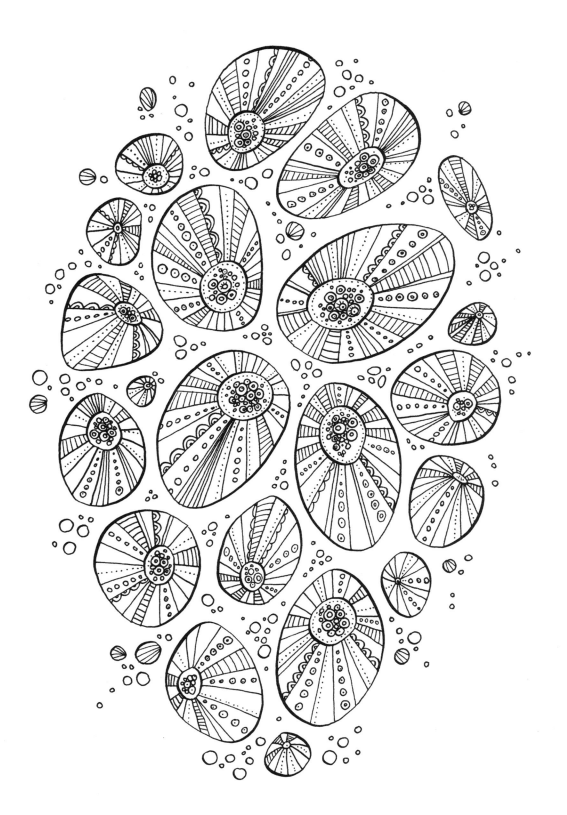

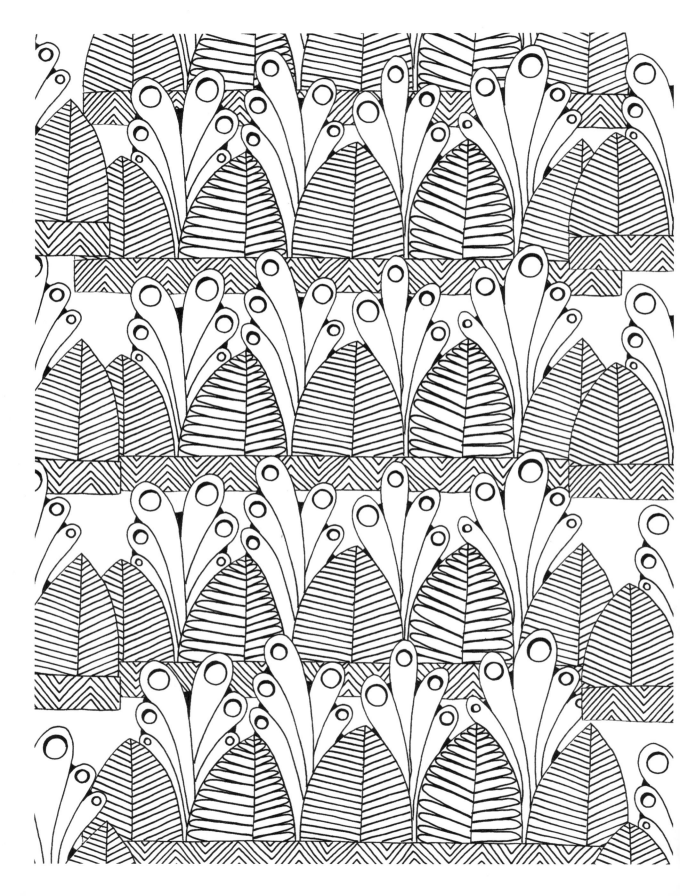